IGOR STRAVINSKY

J̶E̶U̶ ̶D̶E̶ ̶C̶ARTES

Ballet en trois «donnes»
Ballet in three "deals"
Ballett in drei „Runden"

Ernst Eulenburg Ltd
London · Mainz · Madrid · New York · Paris · Tokyo · Toronto · Zürich

CONTENTS / INHALT

PREFACE / VORWORT

Although a number of points remain unclear, the central facts of the genesis of *Jeu de cartes* can be traced on the basis of the accessible sources, in particular Igor Stravinsky's correspondence. The sketch book and the autograph of the score are available for study at the Paul Sacher Foundation in Basle.

The new ballet is mentioned by Nicolas Nabokov in a letter of 11 August 1935; Nabokov had been commissioned by George Balanchine to negotiate with the composer about the ballet.[1] Futher details emerge from a letter by Stravinsky to Balanchine dated 25 November 1935: 'Païchadze [the director of the Edition russe de musique] also told me about the proposal of your company [the American Ballet] to commission a classical ballet from me. The idea is most appealing, but I must warn you that if the project is to be realized, I must be notified immediately so that I may begin work as soon as possible [...] I would like to have now, or very soon, some precise dates for your project, to which I might then devote the remaining free months of the next year. If I begin work sometime in the near future, you could expect to have the piano score of the ballet by the next fall.'[2] On 2 December 1936 Stravinsky entered the first thematic ideas for the composition into his sketch book, including the principal motif of the introduction to the three main sections of the score; he himself connected this motif

Die Entstehungsgeschichte von *Jeu de cartes* kann trotz mancher offener Fragen mit Hilfe der zugänglichen Quellen, insbesondere der Korrespondenz Igor Stravinskys, in wesentlichen Punkten dargestellt werden. Zum Studium stehen außerdem in der Paul Sacher Stiftung in Basel das Skizzenbuch sowie das Autograph der Partitur zur Verfügung.

Im Brief vom 11. 8. 1935 erwähnt Nicolas Nabokov das neue Ballett, über das er im Auftrag von George Balanchine mit dem Komponisten verhandeln soll[1]. Am 25. 11. 1935 sind weitere Einzelheiten aus einem Schreiben Strawinskys an Balanchine zu erfahren: „Païchadze [der Direktor der Edition Russe de la Musique] erzählte mir auch über den Vorschlag Ihrer Gesellschaft [The American Ballet], ein klassisches Ballett bei mir in Auftrag zu geben. Die Idee ist sehr reizvoll, aber ich muß Sie warnen: Wenn das Projekt verwirklicht werden soll, muß ich sofort offiziell unterrichtet werden, so daß ich die Arbeit so bald wie möglich beginnen kann [...] Ich möchte jetzt oder sehr bald einige Daten für Ihr Projekt haben, dem ich dann die übrigen freien Monate des nächsten Jahres widmen könnte. Wenn ich die Arbeit irgendwann in der nächsten Zukunft beginne, können Sie den Klavierauszug des Balletts im nächsten Herbst haben."[2] Am 2. Dezember 1936 komponierte Strawinsky die ersten thematischen Gedanken in sein Skizzenbuch, darunter auch das Hauptmotiv der Einlei-

---

[1] Stravinsky, *Selected Correspondence, ed. and with commentaries by Robert Craft*, London/Boston, vol. II, 1984, p. 312; cited below as *Correspondence*

[2] *Correspondence*, vol. II, p. 314 (original in Russian)

[1] Stravinsky, *Selected Correspondence, ed. and with Commentaries by Robert Craft*, London-Boston Bd II 1984, S. 312; im folgenden zitiert als *Correspondence*

[2] *Correspondence*, Bd II, S. 314 (Original russisch, Übersetzung nach dem Englischen vom Herausgeber)

IV

with gambling casinos in German spa towns.[3] By the time of his trip to South America at the beginning of April 1936 he had already composed a considerable amount of the music up to the third main section. Meanwhile Balanchine was trying to raise money for the project (or find a patron): 'I will make every effort to raise the money needed [...] I like the idea of a classical ballet with a small orchestra, which would make the ballet easier to perform on tour. But I would not want the work to be strictly entertaining in character.'[4]

Stravinsky's ideas about the content of his new ballet were evidently taking shape at just this time. In the same letter Balanchine suggested a dramatization of a fairy tale by Andersen; Stravinsky replied (30 June 1936):

'I must tell you that I have never before composed ballet music without knowing the subject beforehand or having done a preliminary examination of the sequence of episodes of action, consistency, and structure. This is absolutely essential for the general musical structure [...]'

'The ballet I am in the process of composing is not a "divertissement", at least not in the sense against which you warn me. My ballet has a definite and fully intelligible subject with some light intrigue. A normal orchestra is required, a few solo male and female dancers, a single set, and some simple costumes for effect. The length of the piece is between 20 and 25 minutes. The ballet must be produced in the classical style.

'I agree to grant performance rights to your company for one year, under the fol-

tung der drei Teile der Partitur, das er selbst mit Spielkasinos deutscher Bäderstädte in Verbindung brachte[3]. Bis zur Abreise nach Südamerika Anfang April 1936 hatte Strawinsky bereits größere Teile der Musik zum ersten bis dritten Teil komponiert. Während dieser Zeit versuchte Balanchine, das Geld für den geplanten Auftrag zu verdienen bzw. Mäzene zu gewinnen: „Ich unternehme jede Anstrengung, um das nötige Geld aufzutreiben [...] Mir gefällt die Idee eines klassischen Balletts mit kleinem Orchester, so daß das Ballett auf Tourneen leichter aufzuführen wäre. Aber ich möchte kein Werk mit absolut unterhaltendem Charakter."[4]

Strawinsky, dessen Vorstellungen bezüglich des Inhalts seines neuen Balletts offenbar damals gerade erst Gestalt annahmen, erhielt in dem gleichen Brief von Balanchine den Vorschlag, ein Märchen von Andersen zu dramatisieren. Darauf antwortete er am 30. 6. 1936:

„Ich muß Ihnen mitteilen, daß ich nie zuvor Ballettmusik komponierte, ohne das Thema im voraus zu kennen oder zuvor die Folge der Handlungsepisoden, ihre Folgerichtigkeit und Struktur untersucht zu haben. Das ist absolut unentbehrlich für die allgemeine musikalische Struktur [...]

Das Ballett, an dem ich komponiere, ist kein Divertissement, jedenfalls nicht in dem Sinne, vor dem Sie mich warnen. Mein Ballett hat ein klares und ganz verständliches Thema mit einer einfachen Intrige. Ein normales Orchester ist verlangt, einige männliche und weibliche Solotänzer, ein Bühnenbild und einige effektvolle Kostüme. Die Dauer des Stückes beträgt zwischen 20 und 25 Minuten. Das Ballett muß im klassischen Stil inszeniert werden.

Ich bin einverstanden, Ihrer Gesellschaft die Aufführungen für ein Jahr einzu-

[3] cf. *Correspondence*, vol. II, p. 313 and facsimile, p. XXI
[4] Letter, 11 June 1936; *Correspondence*, vol. II, p. 315 (original in Russian)

[3] vgl. *Correspondence,* Bd II, S. 313 und Faksimile S. XXI
[4] Brief vom 11. 6. 1936; *Correspondence,* Bd II, S. 315 (Original russisch)

lowing terms: (1) a payment of $3,000 to me for the world première; (2) a guarantee of a minimum of five performances, at $100 each – this is for royalties and rental of the score; (3) a payment of $700 to me for each of the first three performances that I conduct, i.e., a total of $2,100; (4) payment to my son Theodore (who has designed the set and costumes) of $500 for reproduction rights.'[5]

Negotiations followed by letter between Stravinsky and representatives of the American Ballet concerning payment for the first performance, to be conducted by the composer, and first-year performance rights. Although the ballet is described in the literature as a commission by the American Ballet, Lincoln Kirstein and Balanchine, Stravinsky himself did not regard it as such, on the grounds that he had sold the performing rights for only one year and only for America.

In 1936, at a time when a significant proportion of the music had already been composed, Stravinsky tried without success to persuade Jean Cocteau to collaborate on the scenario. He then turned to Nikita Malayev, a friend of his son Soulima, and Malayev helped him in working out a scenario. In an undated note[6] Stravinsky wrote: 'More than a decade prior to the composition of *Jeu de cartes*, I had an idea for a ballet in which dancers dressed like playing cards would perform against a gambling-table backdrop of green baize. I have always been attracted to card games [...] *Jeu de cartes* was composed at a time when poker was one of my favorite recreations. The origins of the ballet, in the sense of the attraction of the subject, antedate my knowledge of cards,

räumen unter folgenden Bedingungen: (1.) die Zahlung von 3000 $ für die Weltpremiere; (2.) eine Garantie von mindestens fünf Aufführungen für je 100 $ – das ist Autorenhonorar und Leihgebühr für die Partitur; (3.) die Zahlung von 700 $ an mich für jede der ersten drei Aufführungen, die ich dirigiere, d. h. zusammen 2100 $; (4.) Zahlung von 500 $ an meinen Sohn Theodore (der das Bühnenbild und die Kostüme entworfen hat) für die Reproduktionsrechte."[5]

Es erfolgten Verhandlungen in Briefen zwischen Verantwortlichen des American Ballet und Strawinsky über die Vergütung der durch den Komponisten zu dirigierenden Uraufführung und der Bühnenaufführungsrechte für das erste Jahr. Zwar wird das Ballett in der Literatur als Auftragswerk des American Ballet, Lincoln Kirsteins und Balanchines bezeichnet, aber Strawinsky selbst sah es nicht als solches an, da er lediglich die Bühnenaufführungsrechte für ein Jahr und nur für Amerika verkauft habe.

Strawinsky versuchte im Jahre 1936, zu einer Zeit, als bereits ein bedeutender Teil der Musik komponiert war, Jean Cocteau für eine Zusammenarbeit an dem Szenario zu gewinnen, hatte hiermit aber keinen Erfolg. Deshalb wandte er sich an Nikita Malajew, einen Freund seines Sohnes Soulima, der ihm bei der Formulierung eines Szenarios behilflich war. In einer nicht datierten Mitteilung[6] bemerkt Strawinsky: „Mehr als ein Jahrzehnt vor der Komposition von *Jeu de cartes* hatte ich die Idee eines Balletts mit Tänzern, die, als Spielkarten kostümiert, vor dem Hintergrund eines Spieltischs aus grünem Fries tanzen. Vom Kartenspiel war ich immer gefesselt [...] *Jeu de cartes* wurde zu einer Zeit komponiert, als Poker zu meinen lieb-

---

[5] *Correspondence*, vol. II, pp. 215–16 (original in Russian)
[6] Notes accompanying gramophone records, CBS 79245/74061

[5] *Correspondence*, Bd II, S. 215–16 (Original russisch)
[6] Schallplatten-Einführungstext CBS 79245/74061

VI

however, and are probably to be traced back to childhood holidays in German spas.'

After lengthy correspondence with Willy Strecker of the publishers B. Schott's Söhne concerning the American Ballet's contractual rights, Stravinsky was advised by Strecker (22 August 1936) to give the première of the ballet in Germany (Hamburg, Frankfurt or Dresden), so that later opportunities of performing the work would not be jeopardised if *Jeu de cartes* were to be performed in Europe by the American Ballet with an inadequate orchestra.[7] On the same day Stravinsky agreed to Strecker's offer that the new work be published by Schott: 'As far as my new ballet is concerned, I am very happy that you display such enthusiasm for it. I take note of everything you say on the matter of its publication through the good offices of your firm.'[8]

Strecker and Stravinsky met in September 1936 and negotiated the publishing contract, which was concluded on 19 September. By now the publishers had already received part of the manuscript and had begun the engraving of the score. Erich Itor Kahn was commissioned to prepare the piano reduction. His first version was rejected by the composer as unsuitable: 'Saw Kahn yesterday with his reduction for the first scene (Deal) of *Jeu de cartes. Anst[a]endige Arbeit aber viel zu schwer!* [Respectable work but much too difficult.] I pointed out to him the drawbacks and indicated a fair number of places that needed to be re-done

sten Zerstreuungen gehörte. Der Ursprung des Balletts im Sinne der Faszination des Themas liegt jedoch vor meiner Kenntnis des Kartenspiels und kann vermutlich bis in die Ferien in deutschen Bäderstädten während meiner Kindheit zurückverfolgt werden."

Nach längerer Korrespondenz mit Willy Strecker vom Verlag B. Schott's Söhne über die Vertragskonditionen des American Ballet riet dieser ihm am 22.8.1936, das Ballett in Deutschland (Hamburg, Frankfurt oder Dresden) uraufzuführen, um spätere Aufführungschancen nicht zu beeinträchtigen, falls *Jeu de cartes* in Europa durch das American Ballet mit einem möglicherweise unzureichenden Orchester aufgeführt werde[7]. Ebenfalls am 22.8.1936 geht Strawinsky auf Streckers Angebot ein, das neue Werk bei Schott erscheinen zu lassen: „Was mein neues Ballett betrifft bin ich sehr glücklich, daß Sie es so begeistert aufnehmen. Ich notiere mir alles, was Sie mir bezüglich der eventuellen Herausgabe durch Ihren Verlag mitteilten."[8]

Strecker und Strawinsky trafen sich im September 1936 und verhandelten auch über den Verlagsvertrag, der am 19.9.1936 ausgestellt wurde. Zu dieser Zeit hatte der Verlag bereits einen Teil des Maunskripts erhalten und mit dem Stich der Partitur begonnen. Mit der Anfertigung des Klavierauszugs war Erich Itor Kahn beauftragt. Seine erste Fassung wurde vom Komponisten jedoch als ungeeignet abgelehnt: „Gestern sah ich Kahn mit dem Klavierauszug des ersten Bildes (Runde) von *Jeu de cartes.* Anständige Arbeit aber viel zu schwer! Ich habe ihn auf den Nachteil einer solchen Arbeit hingewiesen und ihm einige

---

[7] *Correspondence*, vol. II, p. 317
[8] Unpublished letters by Stravinsky in archive of B. Schott's Söhne, Mainz (originals in French, from which they are here translated directly into English). Cited below as 'Schott Archive' (for original French texts, cf. pp.XVIIIff.).

[7] *Correspondence*, Bd II, S. 317
[8] Unveröffentlichte Briefe Strawinskys im Archiv B. Schott's Söhne, Mainz (Originale französisch, Übersetzung vom Herausgeber); im folgenden zitiert als Schott-Archiv (Originaltext der französischen Zitate s. S. XVIIIff.)

[...] It was agreed between us that he will do me a *Klavi[e]rauszug* [piano reduction] for general use (for the *maître de ballet* and accompanist).'[9] On 7 December 1936 Stravinsky wrote: 'I shall send you the continuation of Kahn's *Klavierauszug* and the final part of the piano transcription, which I am in the process of drafting myself to save time.' And on 10 December: 'Yesterday I sent off to you the final part of the *Klavierauszug*, done partly by Kahn and partly (the last section) by me.'[10] Although Kahn had done a considerable share of the work, his name was not mentioned in the printed version of the piano reduction.

In November 1936 Stravinsky had already sent back sections of the corrected score, parts and piano reduction to the publishers in Mainz (up to rehearsal number 70), as well as a further 30 pages of the orchestration. A pupil of Nadia Boulanger named Preger helped him with the proofreading.[11] On 24 November Stravinsky wrote to report that the penultimate instalment of the orchestrated score and Theodore Stravinsky's illustrations for the piano reduction had been sent off. 'When I return I shall deal with the text[s] of the Argument [synopsis] and the Scenario, which are finished but need some more going over, and I shall send you them so that they can be printed in the score (*Klavierauszug* and orchestral score).'[12] On 1 December 1936 he wrote: 'I shall try to send you the Argument and the Scenario for the ballet tomorrow. I am waiting to see Malayev in order to add a few more corrections.'[13] The following day he sent the Argument and the Scenario (cf. p.XIV) to the publishers, 'so that they can

Stellen gezeigt, die neu zu machen sind [...] es war unter uns vereinbart, daß er mir einen Klavierauszug für den allgemeinen Gebrauch (für den Ballettmeister und den Klavierbegleiter) anfertigen sollte."[9] Am 7. 2. 1936 bemerkt Strawinsky diesbezüglich: „Ich sende Ihnen [...] die Fortsetzung des Klavierauszugs von Kahn und das Ende dieser Klaviertranskription, die ich gerade selbst redigiere, um Zeit zu sparen", und erneut schreibt er am 10. des Monats: „Gestern habe ich Ihnen den letzten Teil des Klavierauszugs geschickt, der z. T. von Kahn und z. T. (das Ende) von mir angefertigt wurde."[10] Obwohl Kahn einen erheblichen Teil der Arbeit geleistet hatte, wurde sein Name im gedruckten Klavierauszug nicht genannt.

Im November sandte Strawinsky bereits Teile der korrigierten Partitur, der Stimmen und des Klavierauszugs an den Verlag in Mainz zurück (bis Ziffer 70) und weitere 30 Seiten der Orchestrierung. Beim Korrekturlesen war ihm ein Schüler Nadia Boulangers namens Preger behilflich[11]. Am 24. November kündigt Strawinsky die vorletzte Sendung der instrumentierten Partitur und der Illustrationen Théodore Strawinskys für den Klavierauszug an. „Nach meiner Rückkehr beschäftige ich mich mit den Texten der Inhaltsangabe und des Szenarios, die fertig sind, aber noch eine Überarbeitung benötigen, und ich sende sie Ihnen für den Druck in der Ausgabe (Klavierauszug und Orchesterpartitur)."[12] Am 1.12.1936 schreibt er diesbezüglich: „Ich versuche, Ihnen morgen die Inhaltsangabe und das Szenario zu senden, nachdem ich Malajew gesehen habe, den ich erwarte, um noch einige Korrekturen einzubringen"[13] und sendet die Inhaltsangabe und das Szenario (siehe S. XIV) am

---

[9] Schott Archive (Paris, 22 October 1936)
[10] Ibid.
[11] Ibid. (15 November 1936)
[12] Ibid. (27 November 1936)
[13] Ibid.

[9] Schott-Archiv (Paris, 22. 10. 1936)
[10] Ibid.
[11] ibid. (15. 11. 1936)
[12] ibid. (27. 11. 1936)
[13] ibid.

VIII

be included in the *Klavierauszug* and the score'.[14]

'The ballet lasts about 20 minutes. The lines of verse for my Argument for *Jeu de cartes* are taken from La Fontaine's fable "The Wolves and the Sheep".'[15]

Argument[16]

'The subject of this ballet is a session of poker. Several players are sitting around the green baize table of a gambling hall. The dancers represent the principal playing cards. Each game is disrupted by repeated mischief on the part of the unpredictable Joker.

'After the first deal one player drops out. The remaining two opponents have equal "straights". Although one of them has the Joker, this card is unable to tip the balance.

'In the second game the player with the Joker has a hand of Aces; with them he beats the other two, exultantly triumphing over the four Queens.

'The cards are dealt for a third time. The game becomes more and more heated. This time there is a battle between three "flushes". The Joker, heading a sequence of Spades, defeats one opponent; but then he himself is beaten by a royal flush in Hearts. This puts an end to the rascally Joker's mischief.

'What does La Fontaine say?
"We must forever wage war on the wicked.
Peace is very good in itself, I agree;
But how can it help
Against deceitful enemies?"'

[14] Ibid.
[15] Ibid. (10 December 1936)
[16] Printed in piano reduction, ED 3296

folgenden Tag an den Verlag, „um sie im Klavierauszug und in der Partitur abzudrucken"[14].

„Das Ballett dauert ungefähr 20 Minuten. Es ist die Fabel von La Fontaine ‚Die Wölfe und die Schafe'. Aus ihr habe ich die abschließenden Verse meiner Inhaltsangabe entnommen."[15]

Inhaltsangabe[16]

„Der Inhalt dieses Ballettes ist eine Partie Poker. Mehrere Spieler sitzen an dem grünen Tisch eines Spielsaales. Die Tänzer stellen die wichtigsten Spielkarten dar. Bei jedem Spiel wird der Ablauf durch die fortgesetzten Tricks des unzuverlässigen Jokers erschwert.

Nach dem ersten Geben scheidet ein Spieler aus. Seine zwei Gegner bleiben im Spiel mit gleichen ‚Straights'. Obwohl der eine von ihnen den Joker besitzt, ist dieser nicht im Stande, die Entscheidung zu bringen.

Im zweiten Spiel gewinnt der Spieler mit dem Joker dank einer Hand von Assen, mit denen er alles schlägt und schließlich über die vier Damen triumphiert.

Es wird zum dritten Mal gegeben. Die Lage wird immer schwieriger. Diesmal handelt es sich um einen Kampf zwischen drei ‚flushes'. Zunächst besiegt der Joker an der Spitze einer Pique Sequenz den einen Gegner; er wird aber schließlich selbst geschlagen durch einen ‚royal flush' in Herz. Dies setzt seiner Boshaftigkeit und seinen Streichen ein Ende.

Wie sagt doch der alte La Fontaine?
‚Daraus nun können wir ersehen,
Daß man beständig Krieg muß führen
mit den Bösen.
Gut ist an sich des Friedens Walten,
Doch kann vom Übel er erlösen
Wenn nicht ihr Wort die Feinde halten?"'

[14] ibid.
[15] ibid. (10. 12. 1936)
[16] abgedruckt im Klavierauszug ED 3296

Before his departure for the United States on 18 December 1936 Stravinsky asked for two copies of the piano reduction and also asked for the engraved parts to be sent to New York, since preparations for the first performance were to begin. On the matter of Malayev's collaboration, a sentence in the same letter is revealing: 'Please also send me the title page (first page) with the name of N. Malayev, so that I can show it to him and he can be sure that everything is in order.'[17] (Malayev is named in the piano reduction as co-author of the Scenario.)

Later Stravinsky complained to Edward Warburg, the banker and director of the American Ballet, that in the programme for the première Malayev had been named as co-author of the libretto, and he demanded that Malayev's name be deleted for subsequent performances. His justification for this position was evidently the fact that the scenario produced with Malayev was rejected in the course of rehearsals with Balanchine in New York. It was only much later, on 6 December 1937, that Malayev signed the following agreement with the composer: 'I was reimbursed by Mr. Igor Stravinsky for the work I did in connection with the ballet *Jeu de cartes*, and I renounce all author's rights.'[18]

Willy Strecker was firmly opposed to printing the Argument in the piano reduction and the score because, among other reasons, he believed this would place a constraint on stage productions. Stravinsky, however, did not agree: 'As far as your question about the Argument is concerned, [...] I am bound to say that unfortunately I am not entirely of your opinion, and I shall tell you why. The Argument in French and English which I sent you is a *résumé* of my libretto and as such cannot be changed.

Vor der Abreise in die USA am 18.12.1936 bittet Strawinsky um zwei Exemplare des Klavierauszugs sowie um die Sendung der gestochenen Stimmen nach New York, da die Vorbereitungen für die Uraufführung beginnen sollten. Bezüglich der Mitarbeit Malajews ist der folgende Hinweis im gleichen Brief aufschlußreich: „Bitte schicken Sie mir ebenso den Titel (erste Seite) mit dem Namen N. Malajews, damit ich sie ihm zeigen kann und er sich überzeugen kann, daß alles in Ordnung ist."[17] (Malajew wird im Klavierauszug als Mitautor am Szenario genannt.)

Später kritisiert der Komponist gegenüber Edward Warburg, dem Bankier und Direktor des American Ballet, im Programm der Uraufführung sei Malajew als Mitarbeiter des Librettos erwähnt und verlangt, dessen Name müsse bei zukünftigen Aufführungen gestrichen werden. Diese Auffassung ist wohl deshalb zu rechtfertigen, weil das mit Malajew erarbeitete Szenario offenbar während der Proben mit Balanchine in New York verworfen wurde. Erst viel später, am 6.12.1937, unterzeichnete Malajew folgende Vereinbarung mit dem Komponisten: „Ich wurde für die Arbeit, die ich im Zusammenhang mit dem Ballett *Jeu de cartes* leistete, von Herrn Igor Strawinsky entschädigt und verzichte auf alle Autorenrechte."[18]

Willy Strecker erklärte sich entschieden gegen den Abdruck der Inhaltsangabe im Klavierauszug und in der Partitur, da er es u. a. eher hinderlich für Bühnenaufführungen ansah, fand aber keine Zustimmung bei Strawinsky: „Was Ihre Frage zur Inhaltsangabe betrifft [...], muß ich Ihnen sagen, daß ich leider nicht ganz Ihrer Meinung bin und zwar deshalb: Die Inhaltsangabe, die ich Ihnen französisch und englisch geschickt habe, ist eine Zusammenfassung meines Librettos, und als solche kann sie

[17] Schott Archive (10 December 1936)
[18] *Correspondence*, vol. II, p. 321

[17] Schott-Archiv (10.12.1936)
[18] *Correspondence*, Bd II, S. 321

X

What might conceivably be changed in some details – difficult to envisage at the moment – is the Scenario. But this we have decided not to publish in the *Klavierauszug* (nor in the orchestral score). How can I dispense with these few sentences which sum up my libretto so well and which I have brought off so well from the formal point of view, with the nice lines from La Fontaine? [...] It's impossible to omit it and I ask you to print it in the *Klavierauszug*, as was agreed between us.'[19]

A letter of 14 March 1937 from Los Angeles[20] confirms this position, as well as mentioning the plan for the first concert performance in conjunction with the Venice Biennale on 14 September of the same year. This concert was being arranged through Mario Corti, the director of the Accademia di Santa Cecilia.

The first performance, which was given on 27 April 1937 in the Metropolitan Opera in New York by the American Ballet, with the composer conducting (and with choreography by George Balanchine and costumes and set by Irene Sharaff), was a great success. Stravinsky repeatedly expressed his approval of Balanchine's choreography, which was developed in the course of the rehearsals, the composer himself assisting. After the première (which was given with *Apollon musagète* and *Le Baiser de la fée*) Stravinsky had some comments to make on music critics: 'The reviews were fairly insignificant, because in New York the papers never send music critics to ballet productions, and these gentlemen, who of course detest music and my music in particular, were only too thrilled to have an evening off. The public filled the huge Metropolitan auditorium twice over and displayed great enthusiasm for my work. I didn't like the set

nicht geändert werden. Das Szenario kann evtl. noch einige Veränderungen in Einzelheiten erfahren, das ist aber im Augenblick schwer vorauszusagen. Wir haben beschlossen, letzteres nicht im Klavierauszug zu veröffentlichen (auch nicht in der Partitur). Wie sollte ich auf diese wenigen Sätze verzichten, in denen mein Libretto so gut zusammengefaßt ist und die bezüglich ihrer Form mit Hilfe der hübschen Verse von La Fontaine so gut gelungen ist [...] Es ist unmöglich, sie wegzulassen und ich bitte Sie, sie im Klavierauszug zu publizieren, wie es unter uns vereinbart war."[19]

In einem Schreiben vom 14. 3. 1937 aus Los Angeles[20] wird dieser Standpunkt bestätigt und der Plan der ersten konzertanten Aufführung anläßlich der Biennale di Venezia am 14. September des Jahres durch die Vermittlung von Mario Corti, dem Direktor der Accademia di Santa Cecilia, erwähnt.

Die Uraufführung in der Metropolitan Opera in New York durch das American Ballet am 27. April 1937 unter Leitung des Komponisten (Choreographie George Balanchine, Kostüme und Ausstattung von Irene Sharaff) hatte großen Erfolg. Strawinsky hat sich mehrfach positiv über die Choreographie Balanchines geäußert, die unter Mitwirkung des Komponisten während der Proben entstand. Nach der Uraufführung zusammen mit *Apollon musagète* und *Le Baiser de la Fée* äußert sich Strawinsky über die Musikkritik: „Die Presse war eher belanglos, denn in New York schicken die Zeitungen niemals Musikkritiker zu Ballettaufführungen, und diese Herren, die selbstverständlich die Musik und meine Musik speziell verabscheuen, waren begeistert, einen Abend auf dem Lande verbringen zu können. Das Publikum füllte zweimal den riesigen Saal der Metropolitan Opera und war von meinem Werk begei-

[19] Ibid. (15 December 1936)
[20] Ibid.

[19] ibid. (15. 12. 1936)
[20] ibid.

(or the costumes) but I greatly admired the dances which Balanchine had choreographed.'[21] The full score and pocket score were published in Mainz in 1937 by Schott (Edition Schott 56 and 3511).

On 22 October 1937, writing in reply to a favourable report by Willy Strecker on the German première of the ballet (evidently abridged) in Dresden, Stravinsky mentioned Pierre Monteux's intention of giving a concert performance of the work in San Francisco. 'The performance and the reception in London were both absolutely splendid. Only the press incompetent and malicious as usual – not that this affected the public, which gave me a real ovation at the second performance, the day after the publication of the articles in question.'[22] For the programme notes at concert performances Stravinsky had Schott print a list of the component items of the ballet. The following notes were used for the Paris première on 6 December 1937, given by the Orchestre National conducted by the composer: 'Completed in November 1936 and first performed at the Metropolitan Opera in New York on 27 April 1937, the ballet is entitled *Jeu de cartes* and depicts a session of cards in three "deals". The characters are the principal cards in poker, and the game is played on green baize. In each deal the game is complicated by the wiles of the deceitful JOKER, using his ability to represent any desired card, which he believes makes him invincible. The order of pieces making up the ballet is as follows:

First Deal: Introduction
             Pas d'action
             Dance of the Joker
             Little Waltz

stert. Ich mochte die Ausstattung nicht (auch nicht die Kostüme), dagegen bewunderte ich die von Balanchine choreographierten Tänze sehr."[21] Die Partitur sowie die Taschenpartitur erschienen 1937 unter der Nummer Edition Schott 56 bzw. 3511 im Mainzer Verlag.

Am 22. 10. 1937 antwortet Strawinsky auf einen positiven Bericht Willy Streckers über die deutsche Premiere des offenbar gekürzten Balletts in Dresden und erwähnt Pierre Monteux' Absicht, das Werk konzertant in San Francisco aufzuführen. „Aufführung und Aufnahme waren in London glänzend. Nur die Presse, wie immer unfähig, böswillig und übrigens ohne irgendeinen Einfluß auf das Publikum, das am Tag nach dem Erscheinen der betreffenden Artikel bei der zweiten Aufführung mir wahre Ovationen darbrachte."[22] Für die Programme konzertanter Aufführungen ließ Strawinsky bei Schott folgende Satzbezeichnungen drucken, hier wiedergegeben in der Fassung für die Pariser Premiere durch das Orchestre National am 6. 12. 1937 unter Leitung des Komponisten: „Vollendet im November 1936 und am 27. April 1937 in der Metropolitan Opera aufgeführt, beschreibt das Ballett mit dem Titel *Jeu de cartes* in der Tat ein Kartenspiel in drei ‚Runden'. Die Personen sind die Hauptkarten des Poker, und die Auseinandersetzung findet auf dem grünen Fries statt. Bei jeder Runde wird das Spiel durch die Verschlagenheit des hinterlistigen JOKERS erschwert, der seine Macht nutzt, um sich an die Stelle der begehrten Karte zu setzen, so daß er unbesiegbar wird. Die Satzfolge des Balletts lautet:

Erste Runde: Introduktion,
              Aktionstanz,
              Tanz des Jokers,
              kleiner Walzer.

[21] Ibid. (20 May 1937)
[22] Ibid.

[21] ibid. (20. 5. 1937)
[22] ibid.

Second Deal:	Introduction March Variations of the Four Queens Variation of the Jack of Hearts Coda Reprise of March and *Danse d'ensemble*
Third Deal:	Introduction Waltz Presto (Battle between the Spades and Hearts) Final dance (Triumph of the Hearts)

Zweite Runde:	Introduktion, Marsch, Variationen der vier Königinnen, Variation des Herz-Buben, Coda, Wiederholung des Marsches und gemeinsamer Tanz.
Dritte Runde:	Introduktion, Walzer, Presto (Kampf der Pik und Herzen), Finaltanz (Triumph der Herzen).

[Handwritten note added by Stravinsky:] The music of the ballet is to be played without break and, even more important, without cuts.'[23]

Although the performances in Amsterdam and in Switzerland (also broadcast) were very well received, Stravinsky was disappointed by the Neapolitan audience: 'As I foresaw, in Naples *Jeu de cartes* produced a sense of astonishment among the public, which is not very cultivated – it wasn't a reaction based on awareness of what it had just heard.'[24]

The unauthorized abridged performances of *Jeu de cartes* in Switzerland gave rise in 1937 to an angry exchange between Stravinsky and Ernest Ansermet and a severe breach in relations between the two men, which until then had been friendly. The composer's harshest words in defence of his work came in a letter to Ansermet dated 19 October 1937: 'I am sorry, but I cannot allow you to make any cuts in *Jeu de cartes*. The absurd one that you propose cripples my little March, which has its form and constructive sense in the totality of the composition (constructive sense that you pre-

[handschriftlich von Strawinsky ergänzt:] Die Musik des Balletts wird ohne Unterbrechung und um so mehr ohne Striche gespielt."[23]

Während auch die Aufführungen in Amsterdam und in der Schweiz (mit Rundfunkübertragung) großen Anklang fanden, äußert sich Strawinsky über das Neapolitanische Publikum enttäuscht: „Wie ich voraussah, erregte *Jeu de cartes* in Neapel bei seinem sehr wenig kultivierten Publikum eher einen Eindruck des Staunens als eine bewußte Reaktion auf das, was man gehört hatte."[24]

Im Zusammenhang mit den nicht autorisierten gekürzten Aufführungen von *Jeu de cartes* in der Schweiz kam es 1937 zwischen Ernest Ansermet und Strawinsky zu einer heftigen Auseinandersetzung und einer empfindlichen Störung ihrer bis dahin freundschaftlichen Beziehung. Am schärfsten verteidigte der Komponist sein Werk in seinem Schreiben vom 19. 10. 1937 an Ansermet: „Ich bedaure, aber ich kann Ihnen keine Striche in *Jeu de Cartes* erlauben. Den absurden Strich (verzeihen Sie mir das Wort, aber ich kann ihn nicht anders bezeichnen), den Sie verlangen, verstüm-

---

[23] Ibid.
[24] Ibid. (17 November 1937)

[23] ibid.
[24] ibid. (17. 11. 1937)

tend defending). You cut my March because its position and its development please you less than the rest. In my eyes, this is not sufficient reason, and I would like to say: "But you are not chez vous, mon cher, I have not said to you, 'Here, take my score and do with it whatever you please.'" I repeat: either you play *Jeu de cartes* as it is or you do not play it at all.'[25]

Stravinsky also took a strong line regarding his dispute with Ansermet in a letter to Willy Strecker of 3 January 1938: 'After a bitter exchange of letters in which I told him everything I thought, and after my forbidding him to perform *Jeu de cartes* with cuts, he has gone and done it all the same, and has admitted as much to friends, who told me the whole conversation and his view of the matter. The strange megalomania that has obsessed the wretched Ansermet for some time has led him to take up this absurd attitude to my new score.'[26] This letter also mentions the gramophone recording with the Berlin Philharmonic, which was made for the firm Telefunken on 21 February.

Writing to the management of the Tonhalle Orchestra in Zurich on 3 January 1938, Stravinsky made it clear that he was not opposed on grounds of principle to a performance of fragments of the ballet music: 'I grant permission for the performance of the music of *Jeu de cartes* only in one of two ways: either complete, or in separate fragments. In the latter case the title given in the

melt meinen kleinen Marsch, der seine Form und seinen konstruktiven Sinn im Gesamten der Komposition hat (den konstruktiven Sinn, den Sie zu verteidigen glauben). Sie verkürzen den Marsch nur, weil sein Mittelteil und seine Durchführung Ihnen weniger gefällt als der Rest. In meinen Augen ist das kein ausreichender Grund, und ich möchte Ihnen sagen: ‚aber Sie sind nicht zu Hause bei sich, mein Lieber', ich habe Ihnen niemals gesagt: ‚Nehmen Sie meine Partitur und machen Sie damit, was Sie wollen'. Ich wiederhole für Sie, entweder spielen Sie *Jeu de Cartes* wie es ist oder Sie spielen es überhaupt nicht."[25]

Zur Auseinandersetzung mit Ansermet nimmt Strawinsky auch in seinem Brief an Willy Strecker vom 3.1.1938 mit Entschiedenheit Stellung: „Nach einem bitteren Briefwechsel, in dem ich ihm alles mitgeteilt hatte, was ich dachte, und ihm verboten hatte, *Jeu de cartes* mit Kürzungen aufzuführen, hat er es dennoch getan. Dies hatte er Freunden mitgeteilt, die mir vom ganzen Gespräch und seinem Standpunkt berichteten. Der merkwürdige Größenwahn, von dem der arme Ansermet seit einer gewissen Zeit besessen ist, hat bei ihm zu diesem absurden Verhalten meiner neuen Partitur gegenüber geführt."[26] Auch die am 21. Februar für die Firma Telefunken mit den Berliner Philharmonikern eingespielte Plattenaufnahme wird in diesem Schreiben erwähnt.

An die Direktion des Tonhalle-Orchesters in Zürich schreibt Strawinsky am 3.1.1938, er sei nicht grundsätzlich gegen eine Aufführung von Fragmenten der Ballett-Musik: „Ich erlaube die Aufführung der Musik von *Jeu de cartes* nur auf zwei Arten, entweder vollständig oder in separaten Fragmenten. Im zweiten Fall muß der Titel im Programm lauten: ‚Fragmente von

---

[25] Paul Sacher Foundation, Basle
[26] Schott Archive

[25] Paul-Sacher-Stiftung, Basel
[26] Schott-Archiv

XIV

programme must read: "Fragments from *Jeu de cartes*, Ballet in Three Deals", with, of course, an indication of the pieces being performed.'[27]

Jeu de cartes is one of the compositions of Stravinsky's which have run into criticism for their use of quotations or near-quotations. It has echoes of Tchaikovsky, Delibes, Johann Strauss, Debussy and Ravel, makes specific references to *Die Fledermaus*, the *Allegretto scherzando* of Beethoven's Eighth Symphony and includes a brief note-for-note quotation from Rossini's Overture to *Il Barbiere di Siviglia*. Its alleged eclecticism and its 'involuntary concessions to American taste'[28] have been held against it. Such responses, however, undoubtedly underrate a humorous and witty score.

Herbert Schneider
Translation Richard Deveson

Jeu de cartes, Ballett in drei Runden', dazu selbstverständlich die Angabe der Stücke, die man aufführt."[27]

Jeu de cartes gehört zu jenen Kompositionen Strawinskys, die wegen ihrer Zitat- oder Fastzitatpraxis (Anklänge an Tschaikowsky, Delibes, Johann Strauß, Debussy und Ravel, konkret: an die *Fledermaus*, an das *Allegretto scherzando* von Beethovens achter Sinfonie sowie das kurze tongetreue Zitat aus Rossinis Ouvertüre zum *Barbiere di Siviglia*), wegen des vermeintlichen Eklektizismus, wegen ihrer „unfreiwilligen Konzessionen an den amerikanischen Geschmack"[28] auf Kritik stießen. Damit wird die humorvolle, witzige Partitur mit Sicherheit unterschätzt.

Herbert Schneider

Igor Stravinsky

JEU de CARTES

Ballet in Three Deals

Stage action devised

By the composer
In collaboration with N. Malayev[29]

Igor Strawinsky

JEU de CARTES

Ballett in drei Runden

Vorlage für die szenischen Vorgänge

vom Komponisten in Zusammenarbeit mit N. Malajew realisiert[29]

FIRST DEAL

In the first five bars of ⑥ the fifteen characters, wearing dominoes and masks and representing the backs of playing cards (blue in the First and Third Deals and pink in the Second), enter and divide into three groups (Centre and Courtyard and Garden sides).

ERSTE RUNDE

Mit den ersten fünf Takten von Ziffer ⑥ kommen die 15 Personen, die mit Dominos und Masken verkleidet sind und die Rückseite einer Spielkarte darstellen (blau in der ersten und dritten und rosa in der zweiten Runde), auf die Bühne und teilen sich in drei Gruppen (Zentrum, Hof- und Gartenseite).

[27] Ibid.
[28] Mikhail Druskin, *Igor Stravinsky*, Leipzig, 1976, p. 146
[29] Schott Archive (original in French)

[27] ibid.
[28] Michail Druskin, *Igor Strawinsky*, Leipzig, 1976, S. 146
[29] Schott Archiv (Original französisch)

From the first bar of [7] the five characters in the Centre group begin to discard their masks and dominoes (blue). First to appear, simultaneously, are the Queens of Clubs and Diamonds; then the Jacks of Clubs and Diamonds; finally the Ace of Spades.

The Jacks and Queens begin to dance, and their dance continues until [16]. At this moment the five characters of the Centre group come together and remain motionless, while the characters of the other two groups rise and discard their own dominoes and masks, in the following order:

Nine of Hearts, Courtyard side

Nine of Spades, Garden side

Ten of Spades, Courtyard side

Ten of Hearts, Garden side

Jack of Hearts, Courtyard side

Jack of Spades, Garden side

Queen of Hearts, Courtyard side

Queen of Spades, Garden side

King of Clubs, Courtyard side

Joker, Garden side

At the appearance of the Joker the characters in the Centre group give up in defeat and withdraw in succession during the six bars after [20].

From [21] until [33] the Joker, in an outburst of rage, tries in vain to challenge the Coutyard side group. During the five bars after [35] he leaves the stage, making threats of revenge.

The nine characters remaining on stage are unmoved by this outburst of rage. With perfect composure they begin a dance in a cheerful, calm waltz rhythm, and this continues from [34] until [39].

Vom ersten Takt bei Ziffer [7] ab beginnen die fünf Personen der Gruppe im Zentrum, ihre Masken und Dominos (blau) abzuwerfen. Zuerst erscheinen gleichzeitig die Kreuz- und Karo-Damen, dann die Kreuz- und Karo-Buben und schließlich Pik-As.

Buben und Damen beginnen zu tanzen und setzen ihren Tanz bis Ziffer [16] fort. In diesem Augenblick vereinigen sich die fünf Personen der Gruppe im Zentrum und bleiben stehen, während die Personen der beiden anderen Gruppen sich erheben, ihre Dominos und anderen Masken in der angegebenen Reihenfolge abwerfen:

neun Herz, Hofseite

neun Pik, Gartenseite

zehn Pik, Hofseite

zehn Herz, Gartenseite

Herz-Bube, Hofseite

Pik-Bube, Gartenseite

Herz-Dame, Hofseite

Pik-Dame, Gartenseite

Kreuz-König, Hofseite

Joker, Gartenseite

Nach der Ankunft des Jokers geben sich die Personen der zentralen Gruppe geschlagen und entfernen sich nacheinander während der sechs Takte nach Ziffer [20].

Von Ziffer [21] bis [33] erfolgt ein Wutausbruch und eine vergebliche Herausforderung des Jokers gegenüber der Gruppe der Hofseite. Während der fünf Takte ab Ziffer [35] verläßt er die Szene unter Rachedrohungen.

Die 9 Personen, die auf der Bühne geblieben sind, läßt dieser Wutausbruch gleichgültig. Sie beginnen in aller Ruhe einen Tanz auf einen Walzerrhythmus von heiterem und friedlichem Charakter, der von Ziffer [34] bis Ziffer [39] fortgesetzt wird.

XVI
SECOND DEAL

During the march the fifteen characters enter and divide into three groups (Centre and Courtyard and Garden sides).

During the last bars of the march the characters in the Garden side group discard their dominoes and masks (pink), and three Kings appear (Diamonds, Clubs and Spades), followed by two pages (the Jacks of Clubs and Spades).

In the last bar of the march two characters in the Courtyard side group also remove their dominoes and masks, and the Jack of Hearts appears, presenting the Queen of Hearts. She begins to dance her little variation and then makes way for the other three characters of her group (the Queens of Diamonds, Clubs and Spades), each of whom removes her mask and domino and in turn dances her own variation. These four variations are followed by the Jack of Hearts's own variation, a triumphal dance. The four Queens and the Jack then together dance a 'coda'.

The group comprising the three Kings and two Jacks, with a gesture of resignation to the Jack of Hearts, then vanish.

To the resumption of the initial march, the characters of the third group (Centre) discard their masks and dominoes. An astonishing turn of events: the Joker appears in the middle of the group, and he introduces his assistants, the four Aces.

The Jack of Hearts concedes defeat and vanishes.

The Joker celebrates his victory with an unbridled dance and pursues the Queens, who are unable to elude his attentions.

ZWEITE RUNDE

Die 15 Personen kommen während des Marsches auf die Bühne und verteilen sich in drei Gruppen (Zentrum, Hof- und Gartenseite).

Während der letzten Takte des Marsches werfen die Personen der Gruppe der Gartenseite die Dominos und Masken (rosa) ab, die sie verbergen, und man sieht drei Könige (Karo, Kreuz und Pik), gefolgt von zwei Pagen (Kreuz- und Pik-Bube).

Im letzten Takt des Marsches legen zwei Personen der Gruppe der Hofseite ihrerseits ihre Dominos und Masken ab, und man sieht den Herz-Buben erscheinen, der die Herz-Dame vorstellt. Sie beginnt, ihre kleinen Variationen zu tanzen und überläßt danach den drei anderen Personen ihrer Gruppe den Platz (Karo-, Kreuz- und Pik-Dame), von denen sich jede ihrer Maske und ihres Dominos entledigt und ihre entsprechende Variation auch tanzt. Diese vier Variationen werden durch den Triumphtanz des Herz-Buben (seine eigene Variation) beschlossen. Danach tanzen die vier Damen und der Bube zusammen eine „Coda".

Die Gruppe der drei Könige und zwei Buben gibt danach ein Zeichen der Ergebenheit vor dem Herz-Buben und verschwindet.

Auf ein erneutes Erklingen des Anfangsmarsches werfen die Personen der dritten Gruppe (Zentrum) ihre Masken und Dominos ab. Überraschende Wendung: inmitten der Gruppe erscheint der Joker, der seine Helfer, die vier Asse, präsentiert.

Der Herz-Bube unterwirft sich und verschwindet.

Der Joker feiert seinen Sieg mit einem zügellosen Tanz und verfolgt die Damen, die seinen Aufmerksamkeiten nicht entgehen können.

THIRD DEAL

The fifteen characters enter and divide as follows:

Garden side: Joker, Ten, Nine, Eight and Seven of Spades

Centre: Ace, King, Queen, Jack and Ten of Hearts

Courtyard side: Nine, Eight, Seven, Six and Five of Hearts

The characters on the Courtyard side, one after the other, discard their (blue) masks and dominoes and begin nonchalantly to dance a waltz, accompanied by the characters of the other two groups; these latter, however, keep wearing their dominoes and masks. They then return to their starting-point and remain motionless.

The characters on the Garden side (Spades) then take off their masks and dominoes and suddenly attack the Courtyard side group; these, after a fierce struggle, realise that they have no choice but to take flight. The victors pursue the vanquished and both groups disappear behind the scenes.

The Joker returns to the stage at the head of his troops, to celebrate his victory. But he suddenly sees the 'royal flush' (the Centre group), whose characters in the meanwhile have removed their dominoes and masks.

Shattered by his defeat, the Joker collapses in front of the 'royal flush' group, which celebrates its victory in a high-spirited dance, after watching its treacherous enemy being borne away by footmen in livery and wigs.

While the King and Queen of Hearts are crowned by the Ace of Hearts, the members of the Courtyard side group of Hearts return to the stage, join the Centre group and dance with them.

DRITTE RUNDE

Die 15 Personen kommen auf die Bühne und verteilen sich folgendermaßen:

Gartenseite: Joker, Pik 10, 9, 8 und 7

Zentrum: Herz As, König, Dame, Bube, 10

Hofseite: Herz 9, 8, 7, 6 und 5

Die Personen der Hofseite legen eine nach der anderen ihre Masken und Dominos (blau) ab und beginnen, unbekümmert einen Walzer in Begleitung der Personen der beiden anderen Gruppen zu tanzen, die Dominos und Masken tragen; nach der Ruckkehr auf ihre Ausgangsplätze bleiben sie stehen.

Dann legen die Personen der Gartenseite (Pik) ihre Masken und Dominos ab und greifen die Gruppe der Hofseite an, die sich nach hartnäckigem Kampf gezwungen sieht, die Flucht zu ergreifen. Die Sieger verfolgen die Besiegten und verschwinden mit ihnen hinter der Kulisse.

Nach der Rückkehr auf die Bühne an der Spitze seiner Truppen, um seinen Triumph zu feiern, bemerkt der Joker plötzlich den „flush royal" (die Gruppe im Zentrum), dessen Personen inzwischen ihre Dominos und Masken abgelegt haben.

Niedergeschmettert durch seine Niederlage bricht der Joker vor der Gruppe des „flush royal" zusammen, die ihren Sieg mit einem fröhlichen Tanz feiert, nachdem sie gesehen hat, wie ihr heimtückischer Gegner von Dienern in Livree und Perücke weggetragen wird.

Während Herz-König und -Dame sich durch das Herz-As krönen lassen, kehrt die Herz-Gruppe der Hofseite auf die Bühne zurück, um sich der Truppe des Zentrums anzuschließen und mit ihr zu tanzen.

[8] «En ce qui concerne mon nouveau ballet je suis très heureux de vous voir y témoigner tellement d'enthousiasme. Je prends note de tout ce que vous me dites au sujet de son édition éventuelle par les soins de votre maison.»

[9] «Vu hier Kahn avec sa réduction du premier tableau (donne) de *Jeu de cartes*. Anst[a]endige Arbeit aber viel zu schwer! Je lui ai fait remarqué[sic] l'inconvenient d'un pareil travail et lui ai indiqué pas mal d'endroits à refaire[...] il était convenu entre nous qu'il me fera un Klavi[e]rauszug pour un besoin courant (pour le maître de ballet et le pianiste-accompagnateur).»

[10] «Je vous enverrai[...] la suite du Klavierauszug de Kahn et la fin de cette transcription pour piano que je suis en train de rédiger moi-même pour gagner du temps.»

«Hier je vous ai expédié la fin du manuscrit du Klavierauszug faite en partie par Kahn en partie (la fin) par moi.»

[12] «Lors de mon retour je vais m'occuper pour les texte[s] de l'ARGUMENT et du SCENARIO qui sont prêt mais qui demandent encore un certain coup de main et vous les enverrai pour l'impression dans l'édition (Klavierauszug et part. d'orch.).»

[13] «L'argument ainsi que le scénario du ballet je tâcherai de vous l'envoyer demain après avoir vu Malaïeff que j'attends pour y introduire quelques corrections encore.»

[14] «pour les placer dans le Klavierauszug et la partition d'orchestre»

[15] «Le ballet dure environ 20 minutes. C'est la fable de La Fontaine ,Les loups et les brebis' de laquelle j'ai tiré les vers pour mon argument du *Jeu de cartes*.»

[16] Argument

«Le sujet de ce ballet, dont les personnages sont les principales figures d'un jeu de cartes, s'inspire d'une partie de poker, disputée entre plusieurs adversaires sur le tapis vert d'une salle de jeux, et compliquée à chaque donne par les constantes roueries du perfide et inlassable Joker, qui se croit invincible, grâce à sa faculté de se métamorphoser en n'importe quelle carte.

Durant la première donne, l'un des joueurs est battu, mais les deux autres adversaires restent en cartes, malgré la présence, chez l'un d'eux, du Joker, qui ne réussit pas à triompher d'un straight.

A la deuxième donne, la main qui possède le Joker est victorieuse, grâce à un carré d'as qui, l'emportant sans difficulté sur un adversaire de moindre force, bat un carré de dames.

Mais vient la troisième donne, et l'action se corse de plus en plus. Cette fois-ci il s'agit d'une lutte entre trois ‹flush› : bien que victorieux au début d'un premier adversaire, le Joker, paradant à la tête d'une séquence de pique, est abattu par un ‹royal flush› de cœur qui mettra fin à sa malice et à ses fourberies.

‹Il faut faire aux méchants guerre continuelle,
(ainsi que l'a dit le bon La Fontaine)
La Paix est fort bonne de soi;
J'en conviens. Mais de quoi sert-elle
Avec des ennemis sans foi?›»

[17] «Envoyez-moi également, je vous prie, le titre (première page) avec le nom de N. Malaïeff pour la lui montrer et s'assurer que tout est en règle.»

[19] «Quant à votre question pour l'argument[...] je dois vous dire que je ne suis pas tout à fait de votre avis malheureusement, et voici pourquoi. L'argument que je vous ai envoyé en français et anglais est un résumé de mon libretto et comme tel il ne peut être changé. Ce qui pourrait éventuellement subir quelques changements dans les détails, difficile à prévoir actuellement, c'est le scénario. Mais ce dernier nous avons décidé de ne pas le publier dans le Klavierauszug (ni dans la part. d'orch. non plus). Comment voulez-vous que je me passe de ces quelques phrases dans lesquelles mon libretto est si bien condensé et qui, au point de vue forme, m'a si bien réussi avec ces jolies vers de La Fontaine[...] C'est impossible de le supprimer et je vous prie de le publier, comme cela était entendu entre nous, dans le Klavierauszug»

[21] «La presse était plutôt insi[g]nifiante car à New York les journaux n'envoient jamais les critiques musicaux aux représentations de ballets et ces messieurs bien entendu détestant la musique et ma musique en particulier n'étaient que ravi de passer une soirée à la campagne. Quant au public il rempli [t] deux fois l'énorme salle du Metropolitan et manifesta un grand enthousiasme pour mon oeuvre. Je n'aimais pas les décors (ni les costumes) mais les danses composées par G. Balanshin [sic] par contre je les admirais beaucoup.»

[22] «C'était très brillant à Londres et l'exécution et la réception. Seulement la presse, comme toujours, incompétente et malveillante du reste sans aucune influence sur le public qui m'a fait une véritable ovation le lendemain de l'apparition des articles en question, à la seconde exécution.»

[23] «Achevé en Novembre 1936 et donné au Metropolitan Opera de New-York le 27 Avril 1937, le ballet qui a pour titre *Jeu de Cartes* décrit, en effet, une partie de cartes en trois ‹donnes›. Les personnages sont les maîtresses cartes du poker, et la partie se dispute sur le tapis vert. A chaque donne, le jeu est compliqué par les astuces du perfide JOKER, usant de son pouvoir de se substituer à la carte désirée, ce qui le rend invincible. Voici la suite des morceaux composant ce ballet:

Première donne: Musique d'introduction,
‹Pas d'action›,
Danse du Joker,
Petite valse.

Deuxième donne: Musique d'introduction,
Marche,
Variations des quatre Reines,
Variation du Valet de coeur, Coda,
Reprise de la Marche et danse d'ensemble.

Troisième donne: Musique d'introduction,
Valse,
Presto (Combat des Piques et des Coeurs),
Danse finale (Triomphe des Coeurs).

La musique de ce ballet se joue sans interruption et d'autant plus sans coupures.»

[24] «Comme je le prévoyais, *Jeu de cartes* à Naples provoqua plutôt une impression d'étonnement dans son public très peu cultivé qu'une réaction consciente de ce qu'il venait d'entendre.»

[25] «Je regrette, mais je ne puis vous accorder aucune coupure dans *Jeu de Cartes*. L'absurde (Vous m'excuserez le mot, mais je ne puis la qualifier autrement) coupure que vous demandez estropie ma petite marche qui a sa forme et son sens constructif dans l'ensemble de la composition (sens constructif que vous prétendez défendre). Vous recoupez ma marche uniquement parce que la partie de son milieu et son développement vous plaît moins que le reste. Ce n'est pas une raison suffisante à mes yeux et je voudrais dire: ‹mais vous n'êtes pas chez vous, mon cher›, je ne vous avais jamais dit: ‹tenez, vous avez ma partition et vous en ferez ce qui vous plaira›. Je vous répète, ou vous jouez *Jeu de Cartes* tel quel, ou vous ne le jouez pas du tout.»

[26] «Après un échange de lettres amères où je lui avais dit tout ce que je pensais et après lui avoir défendu de jouer *Jeu de Cartes* avec des coupures il les avait fait quand même, chose qu'il avoua à des amis qui me racontèrent toute

la conversation et son poi[n]t de vue. L'étrange mégalomanie dont est obsédé ce pauvre Ansermet depuis un certain temps l'a conduit à cette absurde attitude devant ma nouvelle partition.»

[27] «Je n'admets l'exécution de la musique de Jeu de Cartes que de deux façons, ou intégralement ou en fragments séparés. Dans le deuxième cas le titre dans le programme devra porter: ‹Fragments de *Jeu de Cartes*, ballet en trois donnes›, avec bien entendu, l'indication des morceaux que l'on exécute.»

[29] «Igor Stravinsky

JEU DE CARTES

Ballet en trois donnes

Les mouvements scéniques-réalisés par l'auteur en collaboration avec N. Malaïeff.

PREMIERE DONNE

Aves les cinq premières mesures du ⑥, les quinze personnages, revêtus de dominos et de masques, représentant l'envers d'une carte (bleus pour la première et troisième donnes et rose pour la deuxième), entrent en scène, et se divisent en trois groupes (centre, cour et jardin).

Dès la première mesure du ⑦, les cinq personnages du groupe central se mettent à rejeter leurs masques et leurs dominos; (bleus). D'abord, apparaissent simultanément les dames de trèfle et de carreaux ensuite les valets de trèfle et de carreau; et enfin, l'as de pique.

Valets et dames se mettent à danser, et continuent leur danse jusqu'au ⑯. A ce moment, les cinq personnages du groupe central se réunissent et s'immobilisent, tandis que les personnages des deux autres groupes se révèlent, en rejetant leurs dominos et leurs masques dans l'ordre suivant:

Neuf de coeur, côté cour

Neuf de pique, côté jardin

Dix de pique, côté cour

Dix de coeur, côté jardin

Valet de coeur, côté cour

Valet de pique, côté jardin

Dame de coeur, côté cour

Dame de pique, côté jardin

Roi de trèfle, côte cour

Joker, côté jardin

Aussitôt le Joker apparu, les personnages du groupe central s'avouent vaincus, et s'éloignent l'un après l'autre, durant les six mesures du ⎡20⎤.

Du ⎡21⎤ au ⎡33⎤, explosion de rage et de défit impuissant du Joker, contre le groupe côté cour. Pendant les cinq mesures du ⎡33⎤, il quitte la scène avec des menaces de vengeance.

Les neuf personnages restés en scène, indifférents à cette fureur, commencent tranquillement une danse, sur un rythme de valse, qui se continue sereine et paisible du ⎡32⎤ au ⎡39⎤ inclus.

DEUXIEME DONNE

Les quinze personnages entrent en scène au son de la Marche, et se répartissent en trois groupes (centre, côté cour et côté jardin).

Pendant les dernières mesures de la Marche, les personnages du groupe côté jardin rejettent les dominos et masques (roses) qui les dissimulent, et l'on aperçoit trois rois (carreau, trèfle et pique), suivis de deux pages (valet de trèfle et de pique).

A la dernière mesure de la Marche, deux des personnages du groupe côté cour rejettent à leur tour leurs dominos et leurs masques, et l'on voit apparaître le valet de coeur, qui présente la dame de coeur. Elle se met à danser sa petite variation, et, l'ayant terminée, cède immédiatement la place aux trois autres personnages de son groupe (dames de carreau, trèfle et de pique), dont chacune se débarrasse à son tour de son masque et de son domino, et vient aussitôt danser sa variation respective. Ces quatre variations se concluent sur une danse triomphale du valet de coeur, qui constitue sa variation propre. Après quoi les quatre dames et le valet dansent tous les cinq une «coda».

Le groupe des trois rois et des deux valets vient ensuite faire acte de soumission devant le valet de coeur, et disparaît.

Sur un nouveau développement de la Marche du début, les personnages du troisième groupe (centre), rejettent leurs maques leurs dominos. Coup de théâtre: au milieu de ce groupe apparaît le Joker, qui présente ses acolytes, les quatre as.

Le valet de coeur fait acte de soumission et disparaît à son tour.

Le Joker célèbre sa victoire par un pas échevelé, et poursuit les dames qui succombent à ses assiduités.

TROISIEME DONNE

Les quinze personnages entrent en scène et se groupent de la façon suivante:

Côté jardin: Joker, dix, neuf, huit et sept de pique.

Centre: As, roi, dame, valet, dix de coeur.

Côté cour: Neuf, huit, sept, six et cinq de coeur.

Les personnages du groupe côté cour rejettent l'un après l'autre leurs masques et dominos (bleus), et se mettent à danser une valse avec insouciance, en compagnie des personnages des deux autres groupes qui, eux, gardent néanmoins dominos et masques: puis tous s'immobilisent en regagnant leur place. C'est alors que les personnages du groupe côté jardin (piques) rejettent leurs masques et leurs dominos, et aussitôt attaquent le groupe côté cour, qui, après un combat acharné, se voit contraint de prendre la fuite. Les vainqueurs, poursuivant les vaincus, disparaissent avec eux dans la coulisse.

Revenant sur le plateau, à la tête de son groupe, pour célébrer son triomphe, le Joker aperçoit soudain le Flush Royal (le groupe central) dont les personnages ont, entre temps, rejeté leurs dominos et leurs masques.

Accablé par sa défaite, le Joker s'écroule devant le groupe du Flush Royal qui célèbre sa victoire par un pas joyeux, après avoir vu son perfide ennemi emporté par quatre valets de pied en livrée et perruque.

Tandis que le roi et la dame de coeur se font couronner par l'as de coeur, le groupe des coeurs côté cour retourne en scène, pour se joindre au groupe central et danser avec lui.›

First sketch page for *Jeu de Cartes*, dated 2. XII. 1935
Erstes Skizzenblatt zu *Jeu de Cartes*, datiert 2. XII. 1935

First page of the autograph score
Autograph der ersten Partiturseite

JEU DE CARTES

Igor Stravinsky
(1882–1971)

No. 1392   EE 6780

2

6

8

13

Deuxième donne

23

24

29

Var. I
Allegretto ♩= 58

34

38

44

46

54

Pour la danse, reprendre du [99]

Troisième donne

71

84

93

94

97

100

Tempo del principio (Alla breve ♩=69)

Ces deux mesures sont a répéter pour le ballet mais non au concert

bis